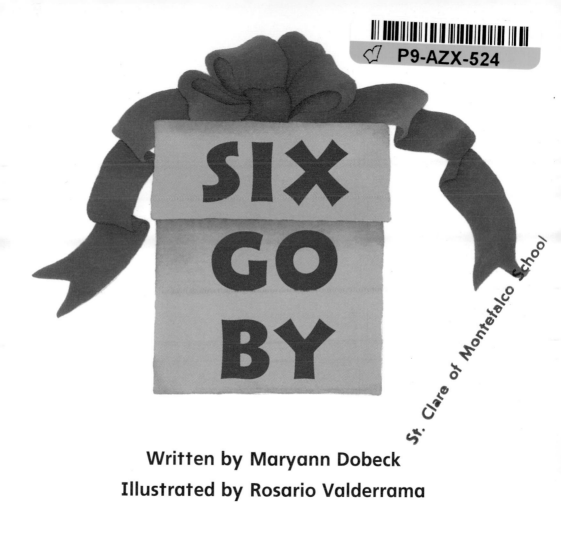

SIX GO BY

Written by Maryann Dobeck

Illustrated by Rosario Valderrama

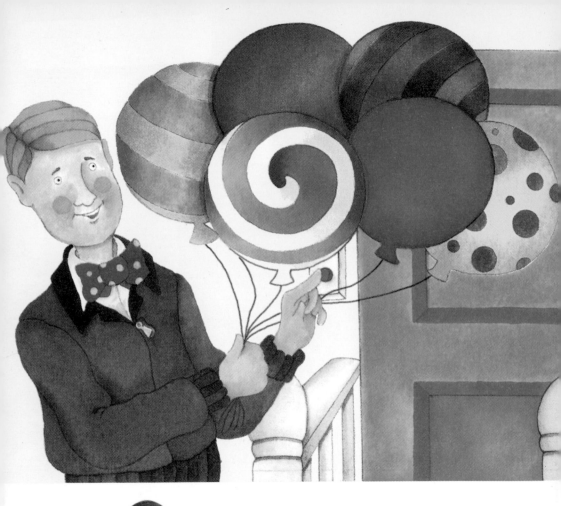

Six balloons go by.

2

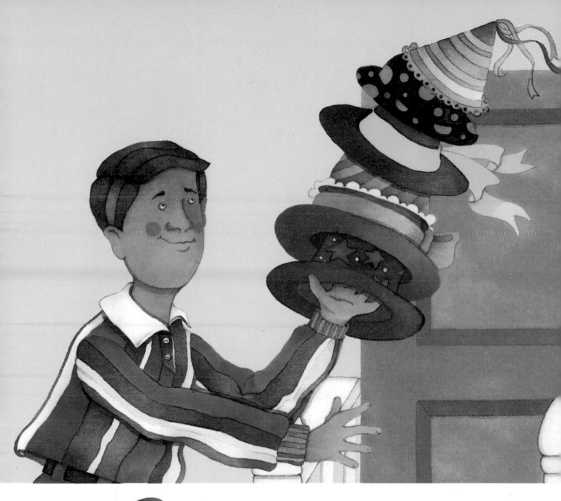

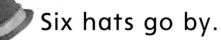 Six hats go by.

3

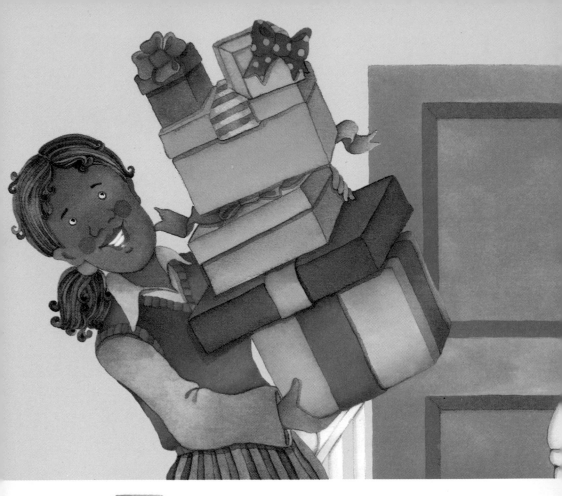

 Six boxes go by.

4

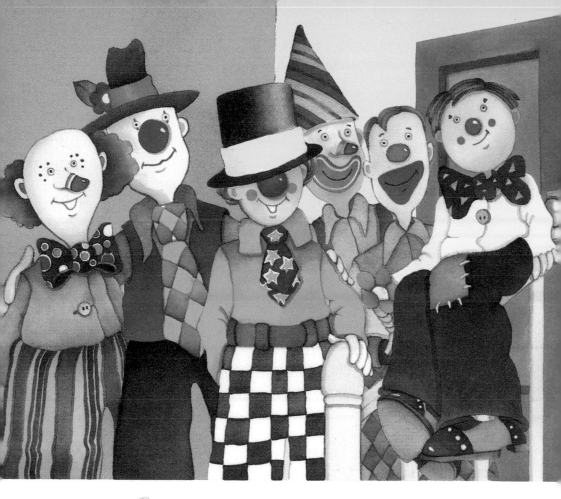

 Six clowns go by.

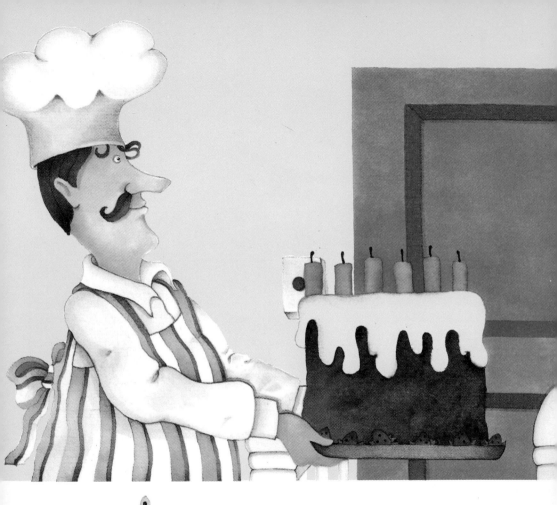

Six candles go by.

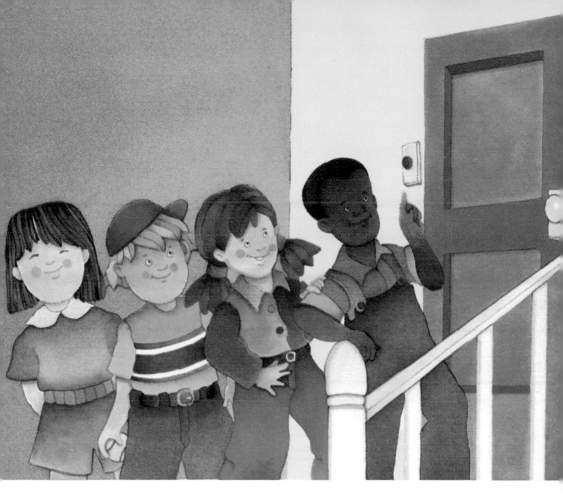

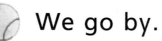 We go by.

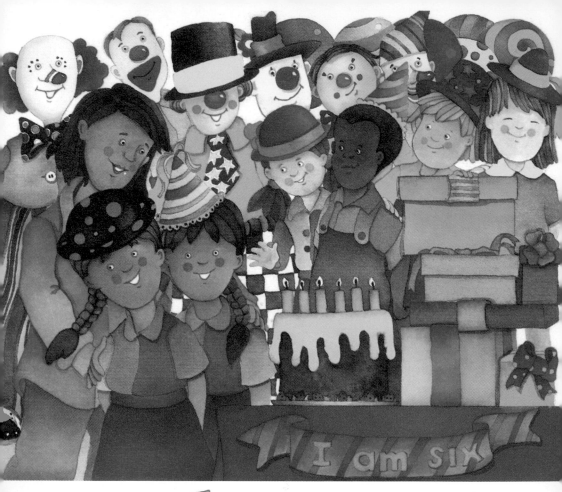

 Surprise!